JACOB
and the
THUNDERSTORM

Written by Brooke Saalman
Illustrated by Edna G. Portillo

Jacob and the Thunderstorm

Brookstone Publishing Group
An imprint of Iron Stream Media
100 Missionary Ridge
Birmingham, AL 35242
IronStreamMedia.com

Library of Congress Control Number: APPLIED FOR

ISBN: 978-1-949856-63-7 (paperback)
ISBN: 978-1-949856-64-4 (e-book)

1 2 3 4 5—26 25 24 23 22
MANUFACTURED IN THE UNITED STATES OF AMERICA

DEDICATION

To my two heroes, Jacob and Hudson, who
have shown me the true meaning of strength
and forever changed my perspective on life and
what is truly important.

Mommy loves you to the moon and back.

For more on Jacob and Hudson's story visit:
www.saalmanstrong.com

Jacob woke up and jumped out of bed. It was opening day for little league baseball! He ate breakfast, brushed his teeth, took a shower and ran to his closet to grab his uniform. He threw on his brand new jersey, pants, and belt. He looked in the mirror and saw that something was missing. His hat! He spotted it on his dresser and plopped it on his head. He smiled as he thought about playing third base in the first game of the season. *If only Dad were here this day would be perfect,* Jacob thought. His dad was out of town for work and was going to miss opening day.

Just as Jacob got his first cleat on, a boom
of thunder shook the house. He jumped.
He ran and looked out of the window.
Large drops of rain fell fast and streaks of
lightning shot across the gray sky. His hands
shook while he tried to tie up his laces.
His head dropped into his hands as his fear
turned to disappointment.

Oh no! thought Jacob. *Opening day is today and now it is going to be cancelled because of this thunderstorm.* His heart fell to his stomach and big, wet tears streamed down his face. Baseball was Jacob's favorite sport. He had been dreaming of the day when he could finally show off his skills in front of his friends and family that were coming to watch him play.

3

Just then Jacob heard a knock at his door. It was his mom. He could tell by the look on her face she didn't have good news. "Hey buddy," she said. "Your coach just called. Opening day has been cancelled. I'm so sorry. I know how much you have been looking forward to this day." She wrapped her arms around Jacob as he cried.

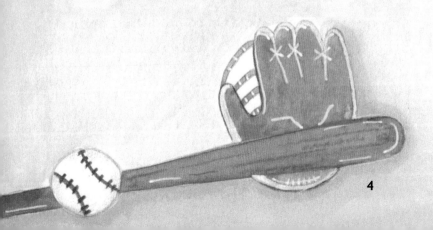

4

"Do you want to talk about how you are feeling?" his mom asked.

"I just hate Thunderstorms!" he yelled. "They are scary and they ruin everything. It's just not fair." Jacob's voice became softer and turned into a whine. He wiped his tears with the sleeve of his jersey. "Why does God let these scary, loud, dark, and wet thunderstorms happen?"

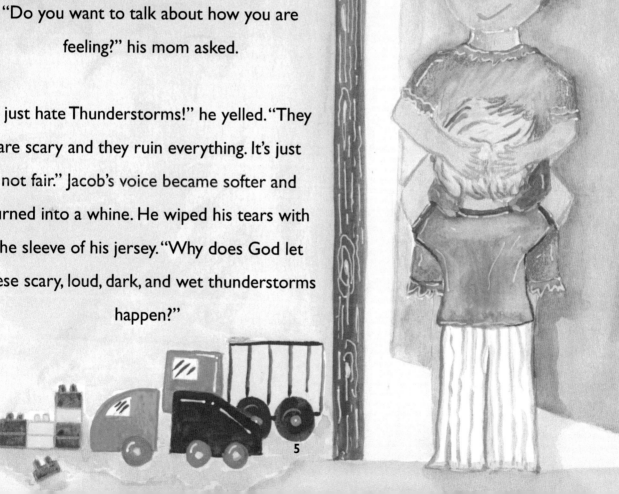

5

"I can understand why you would feel that way," his mom replied in a soothing voice. "But did you know God has a purpose for thunderstorms and He uses them to accomplish good things?"

"Like what?" Jacob said through his gritted teeth.

"Well," she said, "the rain from a thunderstorm cleans out the air. It also provides water to the earth, which is a basic need for all living things and helps them to grow and survive. The lightning is good for the soil and helps plants to grow by creating chemicals in the ground that act as a fertilizer."

"Storms are still scary," Jacob said, rolling his eyes.

8

"There is no reason to be scared," said his mom. "Even though we can't see the sun during a storm, we know it is there. It is still working. It still provides light, though it may be dimmer, and it still provides warmth. We know that the storm always passes and we will see the sun again."

"Well this storm ruined my plans," Jacob replied, shrugging and shoving his hands in his pockets.

"This storm may have ruined the plans you had in mind, but there are many things that you can do during the storm," his mom said. "You can build a blanket fort with your little brother and play some board games. When the storm is over you will appreciate the sun and playing outside even more."

Jacob was really bummed out about his cancelled game, but as he thought about what his mom said, his tears dried up and his smile came back. "I guess you're right," he said. "We can't do anything to make the storm go away so I guess we should just make the best of it."

"That is a great attitude to have," Mom said, giving Jacob a high five. "I'm proud of you."

Throughout the stormy day Jacob, his mom, and little brother Hudson spent a lot of time together. They watched a movie, played board games, read books, and worked puzzles.

Jacob and his brother built a fort and played with many of their toys. They had so much fun that Jacob forgot all about his disappointment.

That night, as Mom tucked Jacob into bed, he said, "I thought today was going to be the worst day ever, but it turned out to be a great day." He snuggled under the covers and smiled.

"I agree," said Mom. "We haven't had a day with no plans in a while. I think it is exactly what we needed. I like to think that when our plans change, it is because God knows what we need more than we do."

Jacob nodded and closed his eyes.

Opening day was rescheduled for the next Saturday. Jacob was so excited, he could hardly think of anything else. The night before the big game, Dad arrived home from out of town. Jacob was so excited to see him! The first thing Jacob told him was that opening day had been cancelled.

"I know you were disappointed," Dad said, "but I am thrilled because now I don't have to miss your first game." Jacob smiled. He had been so disappointed that he didn't even realize the game getting cancelled would allow his dad to be there for his first game of the season.

17

"Wow," said Jacob. "I am so thankful for that thunderstorm! God had a plan all along. Now opening day is going to be better than I could have ever imagined."

"It sure is," said Dad. "God's timing is always perfect!"

19

TALK ABOUT IT

Sometimes things don't turn out like we expect. Sometimes our plans change and God has a different plan than we do. That can be hard and disappointing, but we have to trust God's plan over our own. Many times when we look back on a time our plans changed, we can see that God's plan was actually better than ours. Pretty cool, right? Let's take a look at a verse in the Bible, which talks about His plans for us. It is found in the book of Jeremiah. "For I know the plans I have for you declared the Lord. Plans to prosper you and not to harm you. Plans to give you hope and a future" (Jeremiah 29:11).

We can trust that when our plans change, it is for our good--even if it doesn't feel like it at the time.

Discussion Questions:

1. Talk about a time when you as an adult were disappointed by a change in plans, and then give your child an opportunity to share a similar experience.

2. Think about a time in your life when you made the best out of a difficult situation. Share that with your child and help him/her identify and describe a time when he/she did the same.

3. In a perfect world, there would be something good that comes out of every difficult situation. Sometimes we see it and sometimes we don't. Often we can only see it through the eyes of a child. Explore together with your child some good things that have come out of difficult situations in both of your lives.

4. Did you notice that God might have had a purpose in changing your plans or the difficult situations you have discussed? Take time to discuss what God's purpose may have been.

5. It has been said there are no failures, only learning opportunities toward success. Talk about what you learned from your experiences.

6. The next time God changes the plans you had in mind, discuss how you may handle it differently moving forward.

Lord, thank you for your amazing plans for our lives. Help us to trust that your plans are better than ours even when we feel disappointed by a change in our plans. Amen.

AUTHOR'S NOTE

My two precious sons, Jacob and Hudson, were the inspiration behind this story. They were diagnosed with Duchenne Muscular Dystrophy in October, 2017 at the ages of 5 and 1. Duchenne is an x-linked, genetic, muscle wasting disease that mostly affects boys. It causes global muscle weakness that progressively gets worse over time. It affects skeletal and cardiac muscle. Boys are typically diagnosed around age 5.

Before that life-changing month, I thought I had two perfectly healthy boys. The diagnosis was shocking and heartbreaking. It has been the biggest challenge I have ever faced in my life, and only through the grace of God and my faith have I arrived in a place of peace. The Lord continues to provide me with peace and joy in the midst of this heartbreak. This circumstance has changed my perspective for the better. It is proof that even in the tough seasons of life, the sun still peeks through and rainbows still exist, thanks to our loving heavenly Father who can work all things for good.

Just like Jacob in this story, we all experience "storms" in our lives that come out of nowhere and unexpectedly change our plans. Often times we are left questioning God and wondering why He allowed a certain situation to happen. This is a very real and understandable response. However, what we can learn from this story is that God has a plan for the storms in our lives. He uses them to help us grow, to give us new perspectives, and to accomplish His will and plan for us. Just like Jacob, we can learn to accept the storms and find the beauty that lies within them, knowing that God can do immeasurably more than we could ask or imagine through them and He works all things for our good.

My prayer is that this story will encourage each of us to keep the faith and look past our earthly storms and into the beautiful and eternal story God is writing in our lives.

RESOURCES

To learn more about Duchenne Muscular Dystrophy and how you can help, visit: www.cureduchenne.org.

Cure Duchenne is a non-profit whose mission is to save this generation of children and young adults with Duchenne muscular dystrophy. *Cure Duchenne* is recognized as the global leader in research, patient care, and innovation for improving and extending the lives of those with Duchenne.

ABOUT THE AUTHOR AND THE ILLUSTRATOR

Brooke Saalman lives in Cataula, Georgia, with her husband and two boys, Jacob and Hudson. She received her BA in Early Childhood Education from Columbus State University and her MA in Early Childhood Education from Liberty University. Brooke taught at the elementary level for six years before joining the staff of her church where she served as the Children's Ministry Director for several years. Her boys were diagnosed with Duchenne Muscular Dystrophy in 2017 and soon after she became a full-time stay-at-home mom. She enjoys writing and blogging (www.saalmanstrong.com) and holds a strong passion to raise awareness for Duchenne Muscular Dystrophy.

Edna G. Portillo was born in El Salvador and now resides in Cincinnati, Ohio, with her husband and two children, Sofia and Lucas. Edna received her BA in Visual Arts from Columbus State University. She teaches art to grades K-12 at Liberty Bible School and Montessori Academy of Cincinnati. Edna is passionate about art and enjoys sharing her love of art with students.

Made in the USA
Columbia, SC
14 March 2022

57652680R00018